Do you know your ABC?
Try writing each of the letters
of the alphabet here.

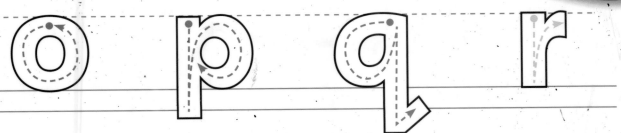

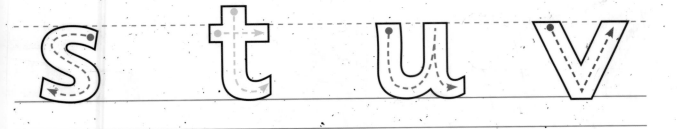

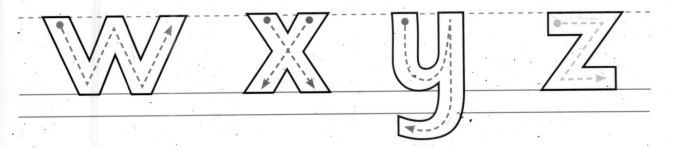

Animal Friends

Ff frog

hippo **Hh**

Pp panda

Write the names of these animals to practise your letters.

mouse _____

Mm

_____

_____

Ss

snake _____

_____

_____

tiger _____

Tt

_____

_____

What's The Weather?

Rr rain _____

_____

sun _____ **Ss**

_____

Cc cloud _____

_____

Write these useful weather words
on the practice lines.

Ww

wind _____

_____

_____

Rr rainbow _____

_____

_____

lightning _____ **Ll**

_____

_____

Snack Time

Aa apple _____

_____

_____

banana _____ **Bb**

_____

_____

Oo orange _____

_____

Learn how to write some tasty treats!

berry **Bb**

Pp **peach**

melon **Mm**

Having Fun

Pp painting

baking Bb

Rr reading

What hobbies do you have?

music

Mm

swimming

Ss

dancing

Dd

Say Hello!

Qq queen

nurse **Nn**

Tt teacher

2 + 2 = 4

Meet some new people and copy
the letters to write their names.

astronaut

Aa

Ww waiter

dentist

Dd

Drawing Shapes

Have fun joining the dots to draw these shapes!